# This book belongs to:

_____

_____

_____

Written by Dawn Boyfield
Illustrated by Geoffrey Greiggs

Printed in Italy.
Copyright © dbda 2003

Supported by

National
Literacy
Trust

MARKS &
SPENCER

# Spencer™

## the bear that's always there

New Town

## Notes to parents

This book is part of a series designed not only to encourage early reading, but also to help children to develop emotionally and socially with respect for themselves and others. All the stories have underlying messages and opportunities to talk about ways in which children can lead confident, healthy and safe lives.

## About this book

There's so much that is new in a young child's life and facing new things often causes turmoil and worry. Many children need the opportunity to talk about their worries and be shown ways to deal with them.

This story is about a boy called Smudge Smith's first trip into a new town. It's full of noise and movement. He's nervous about crossing the busy road and then gets frightened as he gets lost in the crowded shops.

Spencer bear helps him to face these things by showing him what to do and building his confidence to face the situations with courage.

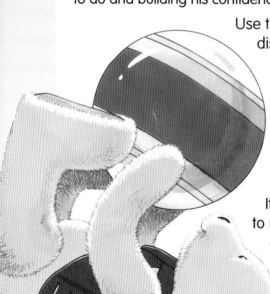

Use this story as a starting point for discussing ways of keeping safe. Make sure they know their Green Cross Code and that traffic can be dangerous.

Make sure they know not to go with strangers, but if they are in trouble who they can and should trust.

It is important that they are able to recite their name, age, address and telephone number.

Practise this with them whenever possible. Remember, give them lots of praise and encouragement to build their confidence.

# Talking points with your child:

**(Choose one or two at each reading.)**

**12-13** • How would they feel moving to a new town?
• Do they live in a built up area or a rural one?

**14-15** • Do they think it's fun exploring new places?
• What new places have you been to together?

**18-19** • What is traffic? Talk about all the different types of vehicles that make up traffic.
• Talk about why traffic can be dangerous.

**20-21** • Point out if they cross between parked cars it's not only difficult for them to see traffic, but for drivers to see them too.

**22-23** • Talk about all the safer crossing places – zebra crossings, pelicans, subways, footbridges, school crossing patrols etc.

**24-25** • Do they know the Green Cross Code, to cross roads safely?
– find a safe place to cross
– stop at the kerb
– use eyes and ears to look and listen all around for traffic
– wait until it's safe to cross
– look and listen
– when safe, walk straight across, still looking and listening.

**26-27** • Why do they think Smudge was scared of crowded places?

**30-31** • Talk about the importance of holding hands when out and keeping in sight of each other and never wandering off.

**40-41** • Emphasise they must never go off with strangers.
• Point out the people that they can trust – police, people in uniforms like security guards, or shopkeepers inside shops. If there's none of these, to look for a mother with children of her own with her.

**42-43** • Talk through what they should do if they are lost.
– stand still, look around and call loudly for the other person
– wait for a few moments
– then look for an adult they can trust
– be able to give their name, age, address and telephone number (practise this with them whenever you can) and praise them when they can manage to recite it all the way through.

9

Smudge Smith and
Spencer were
on the bus.

Smudge looked
sadly out of
the bus window.

10

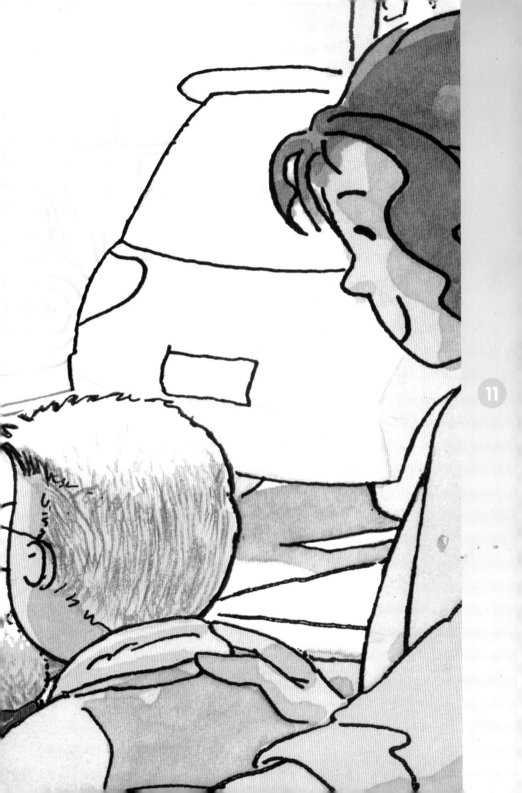

So this was the new town
he had moved to.
He didn't recognise anything.

He just saw lots of traffic
and lots of buildings.
Everything was new to him.
Everything was different, and
there were lots of people.

Smudge was worried, he didn't like new things.

He clung onto Spencer, who whispered in his ear

**"We're wise and kind and good and true. It's fun exploring somewhere new!"**

The bus stopped. Mum,
Smudge and Spencer got off.
They looked all round them.

The traffic sped by very fast.

People hurried here and there.

It was all so busy!

"Now, remember to keep hold of my hand," said Mum.

"We need to find somewhere safe to cross this busy road! The traffic can be dangerous."

They walked along the pavement. There were too many parked cars to be able to cross safely.

Mum told Smudge it was too dangerous to cross here, as they couldn't see the traffic clearly and drivers couldn't see them.

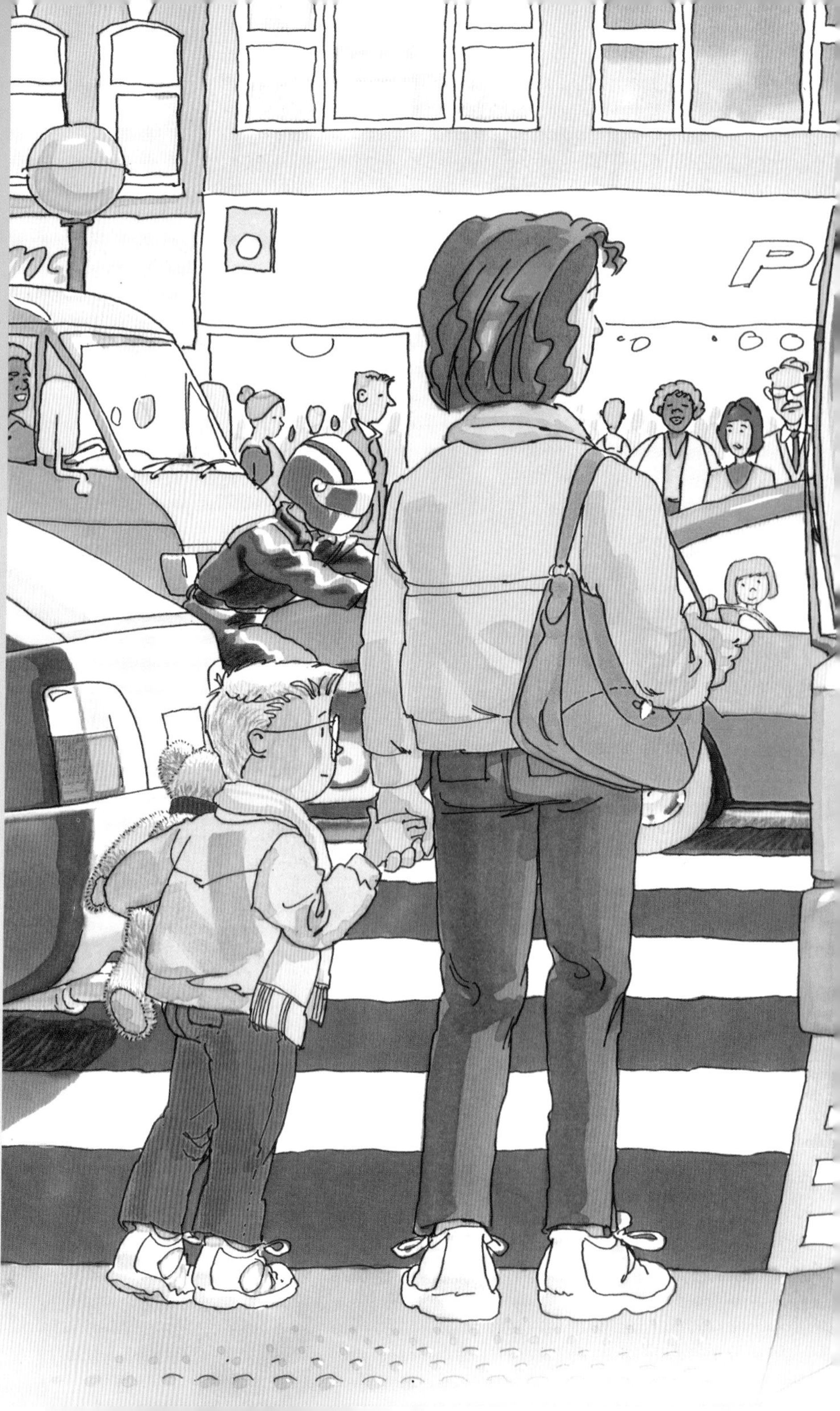

Further along the
road they saw a
Zebra crossing
with Belisha
beacons flashing.

Spencer whispered
quietly to Smudge

**"You're wise and kind
and good and true.
Do you remember
what to do?"**

Smudge grinned
and he said out loud

**"I'm wise and kind
and good and true.
I stop, look, listen,
that's what I do!"**

Mum was very pleased
that Smudge had
remembered how to
cross the road safely.

Once inside the
shopping centre, Smudge
didn't feel very happy –
there were so many people!

He was scared of
crowded places.

28

There were
mums pushing
babies in buggies,
children darting
in and out, and lots of other
people – some talking on
their mobiles, some smiling,
some sad, some frowning.

Smudge looked at Spencer.
Spencer looked back at
Smudge and said

"We're wise and kind
and good and true.
Just keep near Mum
so she sees you!"

Smudge tried to
keep near Mum,
but he was worried.

Mum was already rushing
off to look at a dress
that had caught her eye.

Suddenly, Smudge couldn't see his mum any more.

She had disappeared into the crowd.

Smudge felt very small, lost in the middle of a forest of legs.

He wanted to cry,
but Spencer hugged
him tightly and said

**"You're wise and kind
and good and true.
Don't worry, stand still,
Mum will find you!"**

Smudge and Spencer stood where they were for what seemed like hours, but they couldn't see Mum.

Who could help them?

Then Smudge remembered Mum saying
"Only ask someone you
 can trust to help you."

He asked Spencer
who he could trust here.
Spencer smiled
and answered

**"They're wise and kind
and good and true.
Police will help and
shopkeepers too!"**

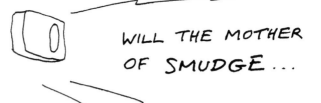

WILL THE MOTHER OF SMUDGE . . .

Soon Smudge
heard a message on
the shop's loudspeaker.

It said "A little boy called
Smudge is lost.
Will his mum come and
collect him from the
Information Desk."

It was funny to hear his
name on the loudspeaker.

44

Mum came rushing up.
She was so pleased to find
Smudge and Spencer
safe and sound.

She said she was so sorry
she hadn't kept them in sight.
She had tried to look for
Smudge, but couldn't find him.

As Mum hugged
Smudge, Spencer
whispered in his ear

**"You're wise and kind
and good and true.
When lost you knew
just what to do!"**

# Oh it's Okey Dokey

Sing it to the tune of 'Hokey Cokey'

**Chorus**
**Oh it's Okey Dokey**
**Yes it's Okey Dokey**
**Sure it's Okey Dokey**
**To face new things each day.**

When you feel the heebee jeebees
And you don't know what to do
You stand up tall
And take a breath or two
Don't let the funny feelings
Get on top of you
That's what it's all about.

**Chorus**

When you want to meet new people
And you don't know what to do
Put on a smile
And hold your hand out too
You're going to make some friends
And you know how to
That's what it's all about.

## Chorus

You have to cross the road
And don't know what to do
Find a place to cross
That'll be safe for you
You stop, you look and listen
And think what to do
That's what it's all about.

## Chorus

When you think you're lost and lonely
And don't know what to do
Find someone safe
To give some help to you
Be sure you know your number
And your address too
That's what it's all about.

## Chorus

## Hello I'm Spencer Bear

Sing it to the tune of 'Grand Old Duke of York'

Hello, I'm Spencer bear
I'm always here for you
You'll see the wisdom and the strength
In everything I do.

I'll always be your friend
And try to give a clue
So when you face new things each day
You'll know just what to do.

You see, you need to learn
That you can be strong too
The strength you need for everything
Is right inside of you.

The strength you need for everything
Is right inside of you.

53